SHIRE NATURAL H

C000212122

THE OYSTERCATCHER

DESMOND NETHERSOLE-THOMPSON

CONTENTS

COVER: *An Oystercatcher returning to its nest and eggs.*

Series editors: Jim Flegg and Chris Humphries.

Set in 9 point Times roman and printed in Great Britain by C. I. Thomas & Sons (Haverfordwest) Ltd, Press Buildings, Merlins Bridge, Haverfordwest, Dyfed.

Introducing the Oystercatcher

In the field the Oystercatcher *(Haematopus ostralegus)* is unmistakable. A large and burly piebald wader, it is about 40-45 cm (15¾ to 17¾ inches) long with a wing span of 80-86 cm (31½ to 33¾ inches). Its weight varies, but it averages between 500 and 536 grams (17½ to 19 ounces) in April. The Oystercatcher's neck and upper breast are jet-black and its wings are also black with a broad white bar. In contrast lower breast, belly and rump are snow-white; the white tail has a broad terminal black band. For the first two years non-breeding birds have almost clerical-looking white collars partly round their necks. The Oystercatcher has a short, sometimes almost invisible neck, pinkish red legs and a vivid redcurrant eye. The orange-red beak is powerful and birds feeding on rocks or hard ground have worn bill tips. The cock's bill averages 69.8 mm (2¾ inches) while the hen's averages longer — 77.1 mm (3 inches). At times, if the bird is running away from the observer, it seems to have a waddling movement. The Oystercatcher's flight is another good field mark; its wings move fast through very small arcs. The sharp excited calls, *keeps* or *keepas,* are also characteristic.

Oystercatchers are found on temperate and tropical shores of every continent except Antarctica. Most forms are black and white, but a very few are completely black (Heppleston, 1973). In *The Birds of the Western Palearctic, Haematopus* is placed between Painted Snipe (Rostratulidae) and Ibisbills (Ibidorhynchidae). J. F. Peters (1934) arranged the genus *Haematopus* in four species with a number of sub-species.

A great pioneer and colonist, the attractive Oystercatcher or Sea-pie has an exceptionally wide range of haunts, wider than any other British wader. Predominantly a coastal bird, it has many breeding places by the seaside. In north Cornwall, in the late 1920s and early 1930s, some pairs nested on high sea cliffs which they then shared with Ravens *(Corvus corax),* Buzzards *(Buteo buteo),* Peregrines *(Falco peregrinus)* and the larger gulls (Laridae). Their nests were well spaced out and often placed on grassy ledges and bluffs. How they shepherded the chicks from such hazardous nest sites is hard to imagine. They also nested on skerries, stacks and promontories along that precipitous coast. On the Isles of Scilly Arthur Whitaker found them breeding in different surroundings on patches of sand, pebbles and grit among groups of rocks. At Ravenglass in Cumbria and at Scoult Head and Blakeney Point in Norfolk nests are on shingle close to Sandwich Tern *(Sterna sandvicensis)* colonies and occasionally on sandhills among small groups of Little Terns *(S. albifrons).* In other haunts nests are on the sea shore or on headlands and promontories or in small numbers on the great estuarial saltmarshes.

In the far north, on Handa Island in Sutherland, Highland, some Oystercatchers lay their eggs on the edges of great cliffs, but on Eynhallow in Orkney they nest on shingle and grass among rocks on the cliff tops as well as lower down the sea shore. They are in good numbers on the machair land of the Western Isles; in 1987 one North Uist nest was in the middle of a bed of nettles (D. B. A. Thompson). Paul Tooley, who found 61 nests in the Western Isles between 26th May and 2nd June 1985, noted that 35 were on coastal habitats, particularly on cliff tops and on sand dunes, 22 on machair land close to the sea and four on inland crofts. Four pairs nested in terneries.

Inland, Oystercatchers choose a still wider range of habitats. The shingle banks and ridges of rivers and lochs are often favoured in Scotland but many pairs nest in isolation on burnt moorland, on newly ploughed, fallow and stubble fields on crofts and farms, and on golf links. A few choose forest bogs or clearings, or exceptionally the thatched roofs of barns or the flat roofs of houses or other parts of ruins or buildings. In 1987 one pair built their nest on the roof of Tain Royal Academy, Highland. At least two of the young reached the flying stage. Nests have been recorded on old jetties, on the rubble beside a railway track and

1. *An Oystercatcher at its nest on a dry stone wall.*

in other unusual places.

The variety of unexpected nest sites recorded on the European mainland is even greater. There Sea-pies have nested on the tops of poles, on wooden fences, on pollard willows, in sandpits, building sites, rubbish dumps, concrete viaducts, old rocket sites, overturned bunkers and small wooden boxes filled with sand. They are also reported nesting in fields of barley, rye, oats, maize, beans, potatoes and Brussels sprouts. Others nest among bushes on polders, in nurseries and in small woods.

The Oystercatcher, so full of vitality and excitement, has attracted the attention of many fine ornithologists all over Europe, including Edmund Selous and Julian Huxley in the early part of the twentieth century, R. Dircksen and Hans Rittinghaus in Germany, G. F. Makkink in the Netherlands, Mike Harris and U. Safriel in Wales, John Goss-Custard in south-west England and Paul Heppleston in north-east Scotland. But this is a wader which can be studied by all birdwatchers in a diversity of haunts. The author has watched them in the farm fields and moors around his home in east Sutherland and on the river shingle and moorland edges of the Spey valley.

PIPING PARTIES

In the 1920s Julian Huxley was among the first to analyse the behaviour and suggest a meaning for the piping parties and sex flights of Oystercatchers. Subsequently other observers have greatly added to our knowledge.

Huxley and Montague described the trilling dance most beautifully in 1925: 'Any number of birds from one to seven, or eight, or possibly more, may take part in it. Typically what occurs is as follows. One or more birds begin the loud characteristic piping which typically again is given in a special attitude, the head and bill directed straight downwards, the bill held open and very slightly vibrated, the neck thrust forward so that the shoulders show up with a rather horsey look. Sometimes, but not always, the whole body is bobbed up and down at intervals in the way common to so many wading birds, but not very markedly.' Often, too, the pipers run in a tortuous course, with short steps, occasionally moving through a half or even a complete circle. Afterwards the piping sounds seem to run down, almost like the sounds of an alarm clock running down, but the birds still show signs of excitement, lifting and dropping straws, stones or other small objects. Nor is the piping ritual restricted to the ground. A pair may fly between two cocks which are chasing one another on a switchback flight, and as they pass by they suddenly drop their necks, open their bills and start to pipe.

Almost any emotional stimulus — sex, aggression, defence of nest or territory — may stimulate a piping performance, which is common to both sexes and even to young Oystercatchers which have barely learnt to fly.

What is the function of this amazing ritual? The author believes that it has been evolved to avoid bill fighting by diverting strong emotions into a harmless ritual. Oystercatchers have powerful and deadly bills which they sometimes use against one another, causing blood and feathers to fly. The piping ritual prevents or helps to restrict this occurrence.

Life history

In their inland haunts on rivers, moors, farms and lochs, early Oystercatchers often return in the last ten days of February. The evocative cries of the first homing birds can then be heard on moonlit nights. A few days later the birds are on the field and beside the river or loch. Soon they will be in the full frenzies of an exciting courtship.

In the Spey valley, Inverness-shire, Highland, the returning birds have no fixed routine. Single birds tend to arrive first and pairs or small flocks or groups follow but in no fixed order. On Skokholm Island, Dyfed, the earliest birds arrive in late February and by 29th March most of the marked birds have been identified. The birds come home between February and March on the German coastlands; and in central Europe they re-occupy their breeding grounds from the end of February to early March.

TERRITORY, SPACING AND BREEDING DENSITY

On habitats with restricted breeding accommodation the territorial drive limits the population. On Skokholm Island, between 12th and 20th March 1968

3 (opposite). *A flock of Oystercatchers standing in the sea.*
2. *A trio of Oystercatchers in their piping display.*

4. *A mixed flock of male and female Oystercatchers on the wing.*

Mike Harris removed one cock and five hens from their territories before laying had started, and between 20th April and 9th May he removed fifteen birds, including the cocks and hens of four pairs. Subsequently, thirteen of the birds which had been left without mates paired with new partners from the surplus. Four cocks eventually re-mated with new hens in one, two, four and four days respectively, thus showing that the groups on this island contained surplus birds which were capable of breeding. The new partners included an experienced hen which had lost her mate, a five-year-old virgin hen and three hens which were then still unringed. Some replacement pairs formed on the territory, but three of the ten cocks whose mates had been removed re-mated with hens stolen from neighbours.

The Dorback groups in the Spey valley held territories of varying size on the shingle and banks of the river and on the moors and fields, but this is not an unvarying rule. The cocks occupy and guard small territories but the hens are less active in their defence. G. F. Makkink, who in 1942 published his fine study on Oystercatchers in the Netherlands,

and Richard Perry, who watched groups in the upper Spey valley in the 1950s, were both convinced that many Oystercatchers were not strictly territorial.

In some haunts, however, pairs defend two quite separate and different territories simultaneously: a nesting territory in which the eggs are hatched and the chicks largely reared within the defended boundaries; and a feeding territory, which may be adjacent to the nesting territory or situated up to about 500 metres (550 yards) away on sea shore or meadow. A parent Oystercatcher carries food from the feeding territory to the unguarded young which are still in the nesting territory. They later shepherd the chicks to the feeding territory soon after they have hatched, unless they are in a nest on a steep cliff.

Pairs scattered over farmland and moor usually appear to have a different system of spacing, apparently relying largely, though not entirely, on the mere pressure of their presence rather than on continuous aggression and firmly defended boundaries. The territorial drive also weakens when many pairs occupy a comparatively small space. True territory does not greatly affect birds breeding

6

almost side by side, like members of tern or gull colonies, but after its eggs have hatched a parent may define and defend the ground to which it has led its brood. However, defence of space und the young on their movements from dangerous mudflats to safer stances does not constitute orthodox territorialism.

Oystercatchers breed at sharply differing levels of density. In the Dorback groups seven to ten pairs nested mainly along the river shingle, each nest separated by 45-235 metres (50-250 yards). On the open moor, however, and on farm fields, nesting pairs were often separated by 400 metres (440 yards) or more. In the upper Spey valley, near Newtonmore, Perry knew of one special length of shingle 250 metres (275 yards) long where seven pairs annually nested on the beaches; some of these nests were sited less than 3 metres (10 feet) apart.

In Sutherland there are contrasts between island and marine groups and those nesting inland. The Handa Island Oystercatchers mostly nest along the tops of cliffs often within 9 metres (10 yards) of the edge. In 1973 two hens were sitting within a space of 3 metres (10 feet). In the south-east of the county, however, Sheriff D. Macdonald recorded that most of the nests were spaced out at intervals of 90-135 metres (100-150 yards). Oystercatchers seldom nest in the deep peatlands of Caithness and Sutherland. The Nature Conservancy Council (1987) recorded breeding on only seven out of 72 survey plots, giving a mean density of 0.02 pairs per square kilometre (0.05 per square mile).

On the Balranald reserve on North Uist Jim Vaughan counted 187 pairs nesting in 1987, with an average density of 24.8 pairs per square kilometre (64.2 per square mile). The highest density was on crops, pastures and fallow fields.

G. Vines found that in the Ythan estuary, Grampian, there were 15.8 pairs per square kilometre (40.9 per square mile) near the coast but only 1.7 pairs per square kilometre (4.4 per square mile) inland, although density was high on habitats adjoining the farmlands, where there were 4 pairs per square kilometre (10.4 per square mile). H. Galbraith and colleagues (1984) estimated that about 2 pairs per square kilometre (5.2 per square mile) bred on Scottish farmlands below 300 metres (1000 feet) and that there was possibly the same density when the Sea-pies were nesting on shingle.

Pairs in Cumbria are well spaced out, with a breeding density of about 4 breeding pairs per hectare (1.6 per acre), though a few nests are only 5 metres (16 feet) apart. Lack of suitable nest sites is probably a limiting factor (G. D. Rankin, 1979).

In 1984-5, in a 2 square kilometre ($\frac{3}{4}$ square mile) study area on the Ribble saltmarshes in Lancashire, Patrick Thompson located 10-15 breeding pairs of Oystercatchers (about 5.0-7.5 breeding pairs per square kilometre, or 13-19 per square miles, as against 168 breeding pairs of Redshanks (*Tringa totanus*) per square kilometre, or 435 per square mile). In both these years two Oystercatcher nests were sited only 9 metres (10 yards) apart and in the same location in both years. This was probably a triangle of a cock with two hens, but it was not proven.

In some of the islands of Schleswig-Holstein the Sea-pies breed at still greater density, with as many as 230 pairs in 10 hectares (9.3 per acre) in Norderoog. Inland, however, the habitats are less thickly populated at a density of 1-2 breeding pairs in 10 hectares (24.7 acres). Some of the small north Friesian islands also have high breeding numbers, with an average density of 3-15 pairs per hectare (1-6 per acre); but inland they are fewer, with an average of 1-2 pairs per hectare (0.4-0.8 per acre).

SEX LIFE AND DISPLAYS

Divorce rates between established pairs are low. Harris (1987) recorded '560 instances where both birds of a pair returned and bred in successive years; in 515 cases (92 per cent) the birds re-united and in 45 cases (8.0 per cent) both birds bred with a new mate even though the first mate was alive but not breeding; and in three pairs both birds were alive but neither bred.' In these groups divorce was commonest among birds of five years of age, the model age of first breeding. Low hatching success increased the chances of divorce. On Mellum in Ger-

7

5 (above). *Ringing an Oystercatcher.*
6 (opposite above). *A clutch of eggs in a substantial nest.*
7 (opposite below). *An Oystercatcher about to sit on a nest on shingle.*

many the divorce rate was only 6.3 per cent in 733 pairs. The longest recorded pairing lasted for twenty years.

From late March onwards, and occasionally earlier, Oystercatchers start to copulate, sometimes while still in the flocks and regularly while the pairs are spread out on field and moor and often far from their own nesting territories. A pair may be feeding some 9 metres (10 yards) apart and then the cock suddenly starts to run towards the hen, calling a series of sharp and distinctive *kit-kits*. As he calls, he runs stiffly up to the hen with his shoulders hunched and his tail slightly expanded and lowered. If the hen is ready to mate she bends stiffly forward with her legs taut, occasionally at an angle of almost 60 degrees, while holding her beak forward and parallel to the ground. Occasionally, perhaps with a hen eager to couple, they run towards one another and the cock passes and encircles

her. Before mounting, he also occasionally stands immediately behind the hen, violently flapping his wings before jumping on to her back, and as he does so the hen bends still further forwards. Immediately before the two birds have joined in sex the cock utters a shrill screechy cry, to which the hen sometimes replies. Lying on her back, legs trailing, he may serve her twice and then the two orange-red beaks may meet in a kind of kiss, or the cock pecks at the hen's crown feathers in ecstasy.

There are many variations of this sexual behaviour. Instead of uttering his copulation cry the cock may 'pipe' up to the hen and occasionally he flaps his wings while mounting her. Afterwards he flounces off the hen's back. Other couplings are less dramatic. The author has watched a cock take his mate while she was sitting on a single egg; afterwards she brooded still more closely. Other hens

8

8. *Oystercatchers copulating. The hen is standing in the 'passive attitude' and the cock with open bill is giving a screechy cry.*

dispense with ritual and merely squat on sand or shingle. Once an observer has watched and listened to the sounds he can always anticipate what is likely to happen. Either sex may attempt to incite the other. Occasionally, too, one or the other adopts the copulation stance in the absence of any other Oystercatcher.

After copulation the two birds show their excitement in many different ways, billing the ground, lifting and dropping grass or straws, making nest dancing movements, feeding unusually quickly, or going through the motions of feeding, or they fly away together or in different directions. In groups of Oystercatchers there are trial marriages and open adulteries. The author observed a strange cock copulate with a feeding hen when her own mate was just out of sight behind a cottage. Makkink watched cocks attempt to rape hens and discovered that hens whose mates were unfaithful attacked the mistresses but not their own mates. The occasional homosexual pairings, he believed, were due to mistaken identity. Oystercatchers are occasionally

bigamous, with two hens laying in the same scoop or almost side by side, exceptionally in consecutive years.

The beautiful butterfly song flight may start from the ground as the bird slowly raises its wings almost vertically before taking off. It then often flies over its territory and its surroundings in a straight line or in circles or ellipses, while giving its song *keep-keep-kweea-kweea* or a series of slow wailing *kweeas*, all the time flying slowly with deep, almost vertical wing beats. This song flight is often used in territorial defence but is not restricted to that. Oystercatchers sometimes sing and make this display flight at night as well as in daylight. 'Whirr' flights are aggressive. Rapidly beating its wings through small arcs, the bird chases trespassers or rivals. Cocks also sometimes slowly fly in butterfly flight in passing a cock or group high in the air.

NEST, EGG AND CLUTCH

From the end of March and throughout April the Oystercatchers undertake spells of nest dancing. At first either bird independently, and later sometimes the pair together, forms scoops by pressing its breast and wing wrists on the ground and scraping vigorously with its feet while its wings are pointed almost vertically upwards, and then it wags its tail from side to side, almost like a nest-dancing cock Lapwing *(Vanellus vanellus)*. From time to time the performing bird stands up and moves to another point of the compass while all the time the nest scoop becomes a deeper and more rounded hollow. The association of the two birds is less ritualised than that of a pair of Lapwings in the later stages of their courtship, but they continue to make scrapes while the eggs are maturing inside the hen. Sometimes the cock stands almost beside his mate while she is scooping, and he may do so when she is about to lay her first egg. She then squats on the empty scoop for up to an hour or more, sometimes longer, almost as if she already had an egg or two under her. Experienced pairs, however, tend to scamp the full nest-dancing ritual, concentrating on particular scoops, in which the hen sometimes lays her eggs in two or more consecutive years.

During nest dancing the performing bird periodically throws straws, small stones and bits and pieces over its shoulders, and some of these are later worked into the lining. The material in the lining varies greatly. At Norderoog on the German coast Dircksen (1932) recorded a nest with 673 fragments of mussel shell in the lining, and in Scotland Seton Gordon found a nest with a mass of burnt heather stalks. On South Uist, Paul Tooley found a nest lined with small sea shells, rootlets and pebbles and another with a lining of road chippings.

These unusual nests raise several questions. Does a hen that makes a substantial nest of, say, flotsam or heather, or indeed do both birds, regularly build this kind of nest? Is this a hereditary practice with the offspring continuing the pattern? Normally, however, nests are sparingly lined with grass, bits of heather, bracken, seaweed, stones, the droppings of sheep, rabbits and hares, and exceptionally cigarette ends or even bird rings.

The laying season varies considerably in different years and locations. On an open stretch of moorland near Boat of Garten, Inverness-shire, Highland, a particular hen, whose eggs were distinctive in shape and markings, annually laid four eggs in each year between 1940 and 1942, at least a week earlier than the average clutch date for the surrounding habitat. A few hens start to sit between 16th and 23rd April on the moorland of the upper Spey valley but groups nesting on shingle banks beside the Dorback Burn had a mean clutch date of 28th May between 1936 and 1942. The lateness of this date was possibly an adaptation to escape from the spring floods and spates which often wash away many nests. On 16th April 1984 a nest with two eggs was found on one of the Shin marshes in Sutherland, but it was considerably earlier than others. Inland groups, Paul Heppleston discovered, tend to lay three or four weeks earlier than coastal birds in north-east Scotland. Island pairs tend to be late nesters; the Skokholm birds usually lay between 1st and 15th May, though eggs are on record in mid March. The Fair Isle peak extends from late April to mid May. On the Isles of Scilly in 1914 Arthur Whitaker and Tom Fowler found nineteen nests between 30th May and 7th June, most of which contained fresh eggs.

Between Ijselmeer and the lower Weser Oystercatchers exceptionally start to lay between 10th and 15th April, and on the northern and eastern Friesian Islands the hens start laying between 20th April and early May, or in late years around 10th May. In Finland some hens are sitting in early May but most delay until the middle of the month. On Kandalashka Bay on the White Sea the laying season is late, with the earliest clutches usually laid between 16th and 24th May and the latest about 25th June.

If the first clutch is destroyed when not too heavily incubated, many Oystercatchers lay at least one replacement clutch, with the first egg deposited seven to fifteen days after the clutch is lost. Some are laid very late in the summer. Hans Rittinghaus found one at Oldeoog on 13th July and another German ornithologist, H. Kumerloeve, recorded a clutch at Arum on 17th July. Mike Harris found that the latest clutch at Skokholm was slightly earlier — 4th July.

Oystercatchers lay their eggs at irregular intervals. Three hens observed by the author laid eggs at intervals of approximately 24-30 hours. R. Dircksen (1932) recorded that most lay their second and third eggs on alternate days with two clear days between the last two eggs. There are, however, probably individual and regional differences. On the White Sea V. Bianki, the Russian observer, recorded that in the fifty pairs he had watched each hen laid her eggs daily with one exception.

The author has been present while five different hens were laying and once watched a cock squat almost beside his mate when she was laying her first egg in a scoop nearby. They do not appear to lay their eggs at any fixed time. Two hens laid their third eggs between 8 and 9 am. Two other hens laid their third and final eggs at approximately 3.30 pm and shortly after 2 pm.

The eggs are usually oval, occasionally pear-shaped and exceptionally they are elongated. The ground colour varies from yellow stone to light buffish brown. A few are reddish and others greenish white. Clutches of unmarked pure white

9 (opposite above). *An Oystercatcher sitting on its nest.*
10 (opposite below). *An Oystercatcher at a nest in grass.*
11 (above). *An Oystercatcher in flight.*

and blue-green eggs are quite unusual but on record. Eggs are streaked, spotted, blotched and particularly stippled and scrawled with dark brown, black and often sepia-black markings with under-markings of umber grey with violet and purple.

One hundred British eggs averaged 56.7 by 40.9 mm (2.23 by 1.61 inches) (Jourdain). 375 eggs from Kandalashka Bay, USSR, were slightly smaller with a mean of 56.0 by 40.1 mm (2.20 by 1.58 inches) (Bianki). The weight of a freshly laid egg averages 46.5 grams (1.7 ounces). A clutch of three, weighing roughly 140 grams (5.05 ounces) is thus approximately 26 per cent of the hen's body weight. An empty eggshell weighs 2.4-3.9 grams (0.09-0.14 ounce), averaging 3.38 grams (0.12 ounce).

A clutch is normally three eggs, occasionally two or four. Smaller or larger clutches are abnormal. There are slight regional differences in clutch size: Skokholm Island, Dyfed, 2.8 (average of 630 nests); inland Aberdeenshire 2.7

(143); coastal Aberdeenshire 2.5 (52); Abernethy, Inverness-shire 2.9 (79); Argyll, 2.5 (65); Western Isles 2.6 (61); Norderoog, Germany 3.0 (100); north-west Friesland, Germany 3.5 (1598); and north-west German coast 2.85 (234). Replacement clutches and clutches laid late in the season tend to be smaller.

INCUBATION

A hen Oystercatcher starts brooding her scoop well before she lays her first egg. After she has laid it, the hen sits for short spells during the day. The author has watched one toying with an egg, periodically changing its position or moving it around. She may also cover and brood a nest containing one or two eggs during the hours of darkness. While the hen is brooding, the cock often stands nearby and later, during incubation, he is often well within calling distance.

J. Keighley and E. J. Buxton (1948) recorded observations at 51 nests, discovering that steady incubation started on the last egg in 48 nests. On two nests it

13

began on the penultimate eggs of clutches of four and on one nest on the second of three eggs.

After the clutch is complete the sexes incubate in spells lasting two to five hours and sometimes more. When incubation is in progress it is always exciting to watch the ritual of nest relief. Before this happens, the sitting bird sometimes pecks and snatches at grasses or stalks around the nest and the relieving bird runs towards the nest in stops and starts, perhaps carrying a small stone or a piece of heather at the tip of its bill. When the sitting bird has slipped off the nest and its mate is settled on the eggs the relieved bird runs away, lifting and throwing bits and pieces sideways before flying away to a distant feeding place. They usually sit lightly, either flying or waddling away from their nests as soon as a watcher's head appears over the skyline of the sand dune or above the bank of the river.

The author measured five incubation periods in the Spey valley varying from approximately 25.1 to 31.3 days, with a mean of 27.5 days. These birds, however, were nesting on sheep farms where they were frequently disturbed from their eggs. Cooling may have contributed to the length of the longer periods. Incubation is usually prolonged if there is much disturbance and the birds are kept off their eggs for long spells. In Germany Dircksen recorded a harassed pair sitting for 34.5 days before hatching their chicks. Another pair in the Soviet Union sat on their eggs for 41 days before deserting the nest.

On Skokholm and Skomer Islands, Wales, Keighley and Buxton give measurements ranging from 25.04 to 28.28 days, with an average of 26.5 days. At Norderoog, Germany, 22 clutches hatched after a period of 26-7 days and eighteen after 27-8 days (mean 26.9 days). At Kandalashka Bay, USSR, Bianki recorded incubation periods varying from 24 to 29 days.

Niko Tinbergen discovered by experiments that Oystercatchers prefer to sit on larger clutches supplemented to five eggs. In another experiment he offered an Oystercatcher the choice of sitting on an egg of its own species, the egg of a Herring Gull (*Larus argentatus*) or a giant wooden artificial egg. The Sea-pie chose the giant egg and made frantic efforts to sit on it.

Sitting Oystercatchers retrieve eggs which have been dislodged from the nest; they do so by standing up and hooking them back with the underside of their bills.

HATCHING AND EGGSHELL DISPOSAL

Before hatching the chick starts to call in the egg and the brooding parent converses with it and its siblings by means of soft *chuk* cries. Hatching is usually a long process, with the chick not emerging from the egg until many hours after the first bump or chip has appeared. The chipping periods of two clutches in Inverness-shire measured by the author were 53 and 67 hours respectively. At Skokholm, Keighley and Buxton worked out chipping periods lasting 1.59 days to 4.4 days (mean 2.9 days).

After the chicks have hatched, the parents usually walk or fly away with large fragments of the eggshell, which they often drop 100 metres (110 yards) or more from the nest. Occasionally, however, they leave one or more of the shells in the nest or they may continue to brood them along with the chicks. Exceptionally an eccentric bird drops a large portion of the shell in a nearby pool and an observer watched one eat the softened membrane. The brooding bird also sometimes breaks large shell fragments and eats the smaller portions, but they appear to leave unhatched eggs in the scoop. The author has seen an Oystercatcher consume the contents of an egg on which a sheep had trodden. Both parents brood the chicks, which are quite capable of leaving the nest soon after they are dry. If the eggs hatch in the evening or in rough weather the parents tend to brood them in the scoop or in its immediate surroundings; they sometimes stay put for two days or exceptionally longer.

THE YOUNG

The chicks are lovely, with blackish crowns tipped with black and grey and blackish grey mantles with light brown tips. Their feet and legs are dull lead-grey with the calves, the back of the tarsus and

14

the underside of the toes dull yellow. They have dark horn-brown bills with a patch of reddish brown at the base.

Oystercatchers are among those few waders, like Stone Curlew *(Burhinus oedicnemus)*, Pratincole *(Glareola pratincola)* and Common Snipe *(Gallinago gallinago)*, which habitually feed their young from the beak. In many haunts the parents take worms from the field and fly over to the chicks with the worms hanging from their beaks. In habitats where the parents eat large insects or on coastal habitats where limpets are a favourite food, these beak deliveries are often less obvious. The parent often encourages the chicks to advance, while still holding the food near the tip of its bill, before dropping it on the ground, or it deposits the food and flies away leaving the chicks to feed themselves. Hans Rittinghaus found that parents often broke up larger items of food on which they themselves also fed, leaving smaller portions for the chicks.

Both parents take part in feeding their brood. F. Goethe (1936) recorded a pair feeding nine-day-old chicks eleven times in eight minutes. They also gave 27-day-old young 114 feeds in 33 minutes. So the parents are kept busy as feeding con-tinues throughout the night. In inland groups the young Oystercatchers tend to break away from their parents after about six to eight weeks but coastal birds, which have to deal with cockles and crabs, take longer as the beaks of the young are not strong enough to tackle such hard matter. Rittinghaus also watched a ringed juvenile in a German group which begged food off its parents until the following breeding season had started. On the German coast observers have discovered that large young are shepherded from the mudflats, where they might drown in floods. Some of these journeys are remarkable; distances of 4.3 km (2¾ miles) are on record.

Chicks take varying, but always long, periods before they can fly. On the Dorback Moor two different young Seapies started to fly on their 27th and 32nd days respectively. Harris recorded 28-31 days on Skokholm. There is a wide spread of periods before they become fully independent.

Breeding success varies, both in different habitats and from year to year. Harris reported that on Skokholm 64 per cent of 291 eggs hatched but only 31 per cent of the chicks finally fledged. The Mellum groups were still less successful.

12. A parent about to deliver food to chicks.

13. *A nest on rocky moorland.*

For every 100 nests an average of only 9.4 young flew; and in some years the percentage was as low as 0.36 flying young per pair. In coastal habitats in north-east Scotland Heppleston found that only 47 per cent of 148 eggs hatched and a mere 13 per cent fledged.

DISTRACTION AND ANTAGONISTIC BEHAVIOUR

Oystercatchers seldom direct elaborate distraction displays at man in Britain, but they sometimes walk off hard-set eggs and then almost crawl or waddle along the ground before stopping and going through the motions of feeding or brooding when well away from the nest. The author saw a sitting Oystercatcher violently flapping its wings while distracting a stoat away from the nest.

Ken Williamson discovered remarkably different behaviour in the Faroes. There the Oystercatchers appeared to treat man as if he was a sheep. They made full use of their colour patterns, creeping away with depressed tails and rhythmically flapping half-open wings, which they trailed when passing over broken ground. From time to time the

bird stood up and came forward with head and beak held downwards, wings spread and tail fanned; they also sometimes mimed brooding.

Oystercatchers are aggressive birds, occasionally sweeping over the head of an observer or, with chicks nearby, flapping their outstretched wings. They also sometimes mob sheep and cattle and often peck at lambs. B. Hoffman saw a Sea-pie rise from its eggs almost under the nose of a wandering bullock, striking the animal with its bill and forcing it to change course. When gulls (Laridae), crows (Corvidae) or raptors fly over the territory the Oystercatcher may fly up and under them, striking upwards at their breasts and bellies.

The piping ritual is often a component of agonistic behaviour. Bill fighting and leap-frogging occur in more serious fighting and the 'wings-up' posture, the 'whirr flight' and sometimes the 'butterfly flight' are also used in aggressive contexts.

BODY LANGUAGE

As probably with all animals, Oystercatchers have evolved ritualised body language which those who watch the

16

14. *An Oystercatcher sitting in a box on top of a pole.*

15. *Oystercatchers feeding on a meadow.*

birds in the field gradually start to understand. Some of these postures have been closely observed, and even given names, by Makkink and other students.

The cock's sexual approach to the hen, already described, has been called the 'stealthy attitude'. In the 'passive attitude', with which the hen shows readiness to couple, she stands stiffly, legs taut, body tilted slightly forward, neck indrawn, bill almost parallel to the ground and tail and rear slightly raised. The 'thickset attitude' is a submissive posture in which the bird's legs are flexed and its neck and head feathers tightly indrawn; beak, back and tail are in line.

Fighting and aggression have their own specialised rituals. An exceptionally submissive bird may mime sleep, open-eyed, tucking its beak under its scapulars or flicking it in and out, or it may walk in the 'hunched posture' with beak, head and tail roughly in line. Other ritualised body language includes the 'crow attitude', a threat posture in which the bird bends forward, elevating head and neck to about 70 degrees and holding its beak slightly downwards while simultaneously slightly fanning its tail. In this posture the bird advances on a rival, holding its feet high. A defensive nuance in an agonistic situation is the 'diplomatist attitude'. In this the bird stands high, inclining at an angle of about 60 degrees with its neck stretched forward and its beak roughly horizontal.

Voice

By day and all through the night Oystercatchers give a great variety of different cries. Some of the basic calls are described here.

The social contact cry, given by both cock and hen, is a loud clear *keepa-keepa* or *kee-eep kee-eep* with variations. The birds utter these calls in many situations, both on the ground and on the wing.

Slightly alarmed birds give sharp *kwik-kwiks* singly or in repetitive series.

The cries of the piping ritual, given by one or more birds during their thrilling display on the ground and in the air, start quite suddenly with a series of sharp *kewit-kewits* and then quickly gather speed and merge into a trill *kee-vit-keev-it-keevee-keeves* before finally sinking into a series of sharp *kik-kiks* which slowly recedes.

A cock's mating cry has been described as a run of single drawn-out *peep-peeps*. The cock's usual pre-coupling cries are a sudden and unannounced group of sharp *kip-kip-kips*. During the act of mating the cock sometimes gives thin screechy cries, to which the hen may respond with similar sounds.

The cock's display flight may start by the bird flapping its wings and singing on the ground before it rises and flies slowly over the moor, field or coast, continuing

16. Sonagram of an extract from the trill of a piping display.

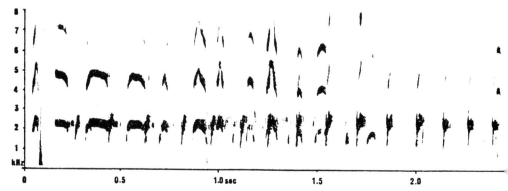

to beat its wings slowly in this almost gull-like flight while giving immediately recognisable series of wailing *kip-kip-kip-kweea-kweea-kweea* sounds, or quite often merely the wailing *kweeas* alone.

Oystercatchers have many different nesting cries, including sharp incisive *pik-piks* when a bird is disturbed from the nest but is not yet too frightened.

Parents give *chuks* to small chicks which are still in the eggs. They also use special cries while feeding chicks outside the scoop. These include a long drawn-out *weep* when flying in with food in the beak and a second call, *chuk*, while on the ground and advancing upon the chick. The chicks give *weep* sounds while in turn moving towards their parents. The cries of the chicks generally resemble the parents' feeding calls, but are softer and less distinctive.

In conflict, Oystercatchers use tinny *toop-toops* on the wing or while attacking or leap-frogging over one another.

Food and feeding

There are great regional and individual differences between the food taken by inland Oystercatchers and that taken by coastal ones. Inland they feed largely on earthworms (Lumbricidae) and, to a lesser extent, on invertebrates, particularly beetles (Coleoptera) and moths and butterflies (Lepidoptera), which they carry in from the fields and pass to their chicks on the river shingle. At Morecambe Bay, Lancashire, P. J. Dare and A. J. Mercer examined the crops and stomachs of 181 breeding Oystercatchers shot inland and found that 177 contained earthworms. As this food is much softer than that taken by the marine groups, the young inland-bred chicks can feed themselves sooner than those on the coast. Otto von Frisch found that after a couple of days his captive birds could feed themselves and that by their fifteenth day they sometimes captured earthworms.

Research suggests that limpet-feeding pairs are less successful than those living in orthodox single defended territories. Mollusc-feeding groups prey heavily on cockles *(Cerastoderma edule)*, mussels *(Mytilus edulis)* and Baltic tellins *(Macoma balthica)*, consuming daily 25 - 40 per cent of their own body weight.

The Oystercatcher is unique among British waders in being considered a serious pest because it feeds largely on cockles in many coastal areas. In Britain peak numbers occur in September when the total population exceeds 200,000. A continuing study on the Exe Estuary, Devon, revealed considerable differences between the behaviour of juveniles and that of adults, and even between that of individuals, and these differences influence the size and viability of populations on the breeding grounds. John Goss-Custard, Sarah Durell and colleagues have studied the way in which three thousand birds exploit 31 mussel beds and other prey, including the bivalve *Scrobicularia plana*, the ragworm *Nereis diversicolor* and earthworms in adjacent fields. Adults, and later juveniles, arrive on the Exe in late summer, attaining their highest numbers in winter. Approximately 80 per cent of the birds are adults and in early spring these leave to breed in the north of England, Scotland, Scandinavia and the Netherlands.

A key aspect of research concerns the possible effects of the loss of estuarine habitat, due mainly to reclamation for industry or farming, and how that would affect the size and composition of the Sea-pie population.

Goss-Custard and Durell found that the most favoured mussel beds (those which provide most food) are closest to the roost. In summer the non-breeders occupy the best beds only; but towards autumn, when the numbers increase six-fold, the birds spread out, with only 20 per cent feeding on the two best areas. Competition apparently accounts for this change, with the most aggressive adults frequenting the richest beds and thus obtaining most food. We know that status has an important role in the tenure of the best beds because some of the birds feeding on them obtain less food than those taking station on the poorer beds.

17. *A group of Oystercatchers standing on the tideline.*

Mortality among immature birds is greater than among adults, suggesting that some displaced birds fail to obtain sufficient food and thus starve or fall victim to predators (Goss-Custard and Durell, 1987). Loss of winter habitats through land reclamation is thus likely to lead to smaller non-breeding populations, with mortality highest in the youngest birds and probably fewer recruits to the breeding population in future years.

Goss-Custard and his colleagues found that in their study areas on the Wash Oystercatchers stopped feeding at night in January and February; but, in Morecambe Bay, M. E. Greenhalgh discovered that they consumed almost 50 per cent of their normal daylight rate of predation on mussels and 19 per cent on Baltic tellins at night. Hale suggests that this may be due to high tide taking place around midday in north-west England. So the Oystercatchers gear their feeding to the local environment. They are hungry birds. Hale has estimated that the groups wintering in Britain require 56 million cockles each daylight tide. Each bird eats about 280 cockles per daylight tide and up to 150 times its own weight per year.

Feeding methods are a special study. The Oystercatchers are likely to locate earthworms on the fields partly by sound, and they stalk beetles and other insects among the shingle. At other times they stab the ground with partly open beaks. Niko Tinbergen and M. Norton-Griffiths found that they probably obtain mussels from tidal pools by stabbing the abductor muscle and then forcing open the valves, and so stripping the molluscs from their shells. At other times the bird hammers the mollusc until it opens. J. B. Hulscher discovered that cockles were hammered open on dry sand and forced open on wet sand. Chicks tend to learn methods from their parents. Limpets are detached from the rock by thrusting at the edges of their shells with closed beaks or hammering them through a crack, if there happens to be one.

20

Predators and pirates

Oystercatchers have many predators in their inland and marine habitats. In the upper Spey valley Hooded Crows *(Corvus corone cornix)*, from the old pine forests, and very occasionally Common Gulls *(Larus canus)* raid nests, and foxes, stoats and sheepdogs periodically snap up chicks. However, compared to the destruction of a severe spring or early summer flood, losses from predators are insignificant. A large spate sometimes washes out almost every nest along a river and drowns almost all the young before their parents can shepherd them away. Peregrines sometimes knock down mature Oystercatchers, but they do not do so on a grand scale. In 1962-3, for example, Derek Ratcliffe recorded only eight Oystercatchers from inland haunts and five from coastal nesting grounds among the remains and pluckings from 144 waders. In the central Grampians, moreover, where Douglas Weir studied the prey of 23 pairs of Peregrines, the tally of destruction was even less; there was only one mature Oystercatcher in 102 wader kills. He discovered, however, that Peregrines prey on Oystercatcher chicks and unflown young. Patrick Thompson found an Oystercatcher's beak in an east Sutherland eyrie and in another part of the county a Peregrine was seen to lift and fly off with a young Sea-pie.

Coastal habitats produce different problems. Some groups nest among colonies of Herring Gulls *(Larus argentatus)*, whose eggs they habitually rob and eat. Later, however, the gulls turn the tables. In the Netherlands C. S. Roselaar studied groups of Oystercatchers in which not a single chick lived to fly — the Herring Gulls had eaten them all. In 1963-5 Harris noted that groups breeding among or close to gull colonies had a success rate of only 50 per cent whereas those nesting well away from gulls enjoyed 75 per cent. Lesser Black-backed Gulls *(Larus fuscus)* prey heavily on the Skokholm groups. They appear to find it easy to catch, kill and eat young Oystercatchers just before they can fly and when they are conspicuous and helpless against attack. At the Hook of Holland Tinbergen (1931) found that Oystercatchers were serious egg and chick robbers of Common Terns *(Sterna hirundo)*, making for their nests when the colony was disturbed and feeding on the guts of tern chicks, which they later fed to their own young. In North Uist Great Black-backed Gulls *(L. marinus)* are formidable predators, particularly on unflown chicks. D. B. A. Nethersole-Thompson watched one fly after three loudly calling Oystercatchers: it caught up with one, pulling off its wing in the air. The pirate then followed it to the ground and started to devour it.

Oystercatchers are sometimes dangerous neighbours to Lapwings nesting in the same ploughed field or open moor. One, whose mate had recently exchanged with it at the nest, ran a short distance and then flew directly to a brae on which a hen Lapwing was incubating. As the Oystercatcher moved in the Lapwing rose from its nest and directed a forward threat display at the intruder. Almost immediately the cock Lapwing flew in and flashed at the Sea-pie, which soon abandoned its attempt at robbery.

Flocking, distribution and numbers

Flocking patterns depend on the feedng grounds of the young Oystercatchers and the time taken to learn to feed and to become independent. Many old birds on the Dorback Moor leave their breeding grounds before the end of July, but groups of juveniles and a few mature birds join up and form small flocks.

Heppleston found that flocks of mixed sexes sometimes roosted together. J. M. Dewar (1915) discovered that there were traditional feeding grounds on the Firth of Forth to which the same particular flocks returned year after year, avoiding those favoured by other groups. P. J. Dare noticed that the largest assemblies of Oystercatchers in Britain consisted mainly of adults of both sexes. E. Hosking and W. G. Hale (1983) describe the flocking and roosting behaviour on the Morecambe Bay, Ribble and Dee estuarine complex. About three hours before high tide the Sea-pies begin to quit feeding and make their way inland to form temporary roosts out on the mudflats. Once every fortnight during the first and third quarters of the moon, the period which produces the highest tides, they roost on the high points of the shore. During neap tides they roost in less packed assemblies out on the mudflats. In the highest spring tides, however, they are sometimes forced to roost on the saltmarshes and may even be compelled to settle for farm fields. The Oystercatchers are the first waders to go to roost, after forming 'a compact group or subgroup an hour before other species appear' (Hale, 1980). Many are asleep when the tide washes upwards and they often hop along on one leg while still dozing, until at last they are forced to find refuge in a regular dry roost on the saltmarsh. Later other large waders follow them to roost but the Oystercatchers and Black-Tailed Godwits (*Limosa limosa*) tend to stay in single-species assemblies.

In winter there are many opportunities for watching the Sea-pies. They are often seen on the sea shore or estuarial mudflats. At low tide they work in small groups, but when the tide rises they merge into large assemblies of a hundred or more. Almost always their evocative sharp ringing calls can be heard, and occasionally brief bursts of the famous piping trills when a few birds bicker about items of food or possibly their status in the flock.

The Oystercatcher is a forceful animal, continually probing, pioneering and colonising inland habitats which were formerly only marginal. This increase has sometimes coincided with local declines of Lapwings.

H. Galbraith and his colleagues (1984) estimated that in Scotland twenty thousand pairs now nest in the ploughed fields and meadows of the mainland and a further two thousand pairs in the machair lands of the Western Isles. About 70 per cent of the breeding population of Oystercatchers in Britain nest in Scotland, where they nest in every county and island group and in all but 25 ten-kilometre squares (Thom, 1986).

The Breeding Atlas (1976) gives confirmed breeding in 1409, probable breeding in 174 and possible breeding in 219 ten-kilometre squares. Between 33,000 and 43,000 pairs are estimated to breed in Britain (Nature Conservancy Council, 1987). This estimate is probably conservative, in spite of massive culls between 1956 and 1974 which accounted for about 25,000 Sea-pies, imposed because of their alleged devastation of cockle fisheries in England and Wales.

Estimates of breeding numbers in other western Palearctic countries are equally impressive. Between 10,000 and 30,000 pairs nest in Iceland and about 30,000 pairs on the Faroes. Ireland has about 4,000 pairs, France 540-60 pairs, Belgium about 100 pairs, the Netherlands 50,000-60,000 pairs, West and East Germany 13,000 pairs, Denmark roughly 5,000 pairs, Norway 40,000 pairs and Sweden 10,000 pairs (Cramp *et al*, 1983).

Prater (1981 and 1983) has estimated that outside the breeding season up to 200,000-250,000 Oystercatchers winter in Britain, many thousands on great estuaries. Movements from breeding grounds to the coast in Scotland start in July and increase in August and September, when the flocks are augmented by immigrants from Norway, the Faroes and Iceland. The Moray Firth, the Eden estuary in Fife, the Firth of Forth, the inner Clyde and the north Solway marshes all hold large groups and populations. In this period many groups from the Forth estuary fly across country to Solway. Then, in midwinter, many move from there to the Morecambe Bay estuarial complex, cross the Irish Sea or go further south.

Apart from the great concentrations on the Scottish estuaries, the Sea-pies also winter in high numbers in other parts of Scotland and the islands: over 2700 in Orkney, 3000-4000 in the Western Isles, and 10,500-14,500 on the mainland and Inner Hebridean coasts between north

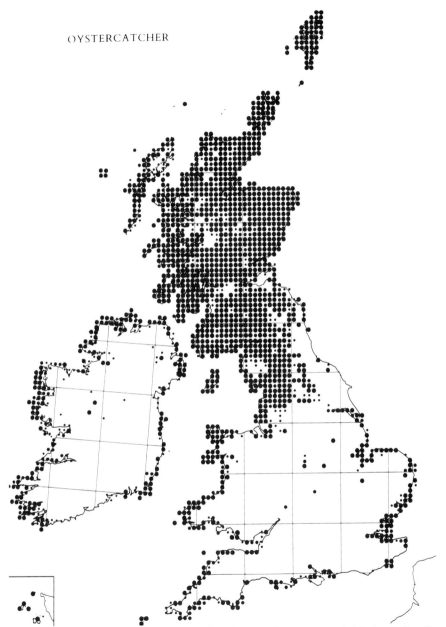

18. *The number of ten-kilometre squares in which Oystercatchers were recorded during the breeding season (1968-72) was 1802 (47 per cent). Breeding was confirmed in 1409 squares (large dots); it was probable in 174 squares (medium-sized dots) and possible in 219 (small dots). These figures represent respectively 78, 10 and 12 per cent of the number of squares in which the birds were recorded.*

23

Sutherland and Kintyre (Thom, 1986). The Wash on the east coast, where 15,000 were counted at Snettisham on 28th August 1986, Morecambe Bay and the Ribble and Dee estuaries on the west coast and Burry Inlet in Wales all carry great flocks.

Some Oystercatchers, particularly those nesting in southern England, winter close to their breeding grounds, but small groups make their way to France, Spain and Portugal and exceptionally to Morocco (Cramp et al, 1983).

Further reading

Cramp, S., and Simmons, K. *The Birds of the Western Palearctic* volume 3, 17-35. Oxford University Press, 1983.

Goss-Custard, J. D., and Durell, S. E. A. 'Age-related Effects in Oystercatchers *Haematopus ostralegus,* Feeding on Mussels *Mytilus edulis.* I. Foraging, Efficiency and Interference. II. Aggression. III. The Effect of Interference on Overall Intake Rate, *Journal of Animal Ecology* 56, 521-8. 1987.

Hale, W. G. *Waders.* Collins, 1986.

Harris, M. P. 'The Biology of Oystercatchers on Skokholm Island, South Wales', *Ibis* 109, 180-3. 1967.

Harris, M. P. 'Territory Limiting the Size of the Breeding Population of the Oystercatcher — a Removal Experiment,' *Journal of Animal Ecology*, 39, 707-13. 1970.

Harris, M. P., et al. 'The Pair Bond and Divorce among Oystercatchers on Skokholm Island, South Wales', *Ibis* 129, 45-57. 1986.

Hosking, E., and Hale, W. G. *Eric Hosking's Waders.* Pelham, 1983.

Nethersole-Thompson, D. *Highland Birds.* Highlands and Islands Development Board. Inverness, third edition 1978.

Nethersole-Thompson, D., and Nethersole-Thompson, M. *Waders: Their Breeding, Haunts and Watchers.* Poyser, Calton, 1986.

Prater, A. J. *Estuary Birds of Britain and Ireland.* Poyser, Calton, 1981.

Thom, V. *Birds in Scotland.* Poyser, Calton, 1986.

ACKNOWLEDGEMENTS

The author wishes to thank his sons, Bruin and Patrick, Paul Tooley and Jim Vaughan for unpublished material. He is grateful to Mr and Mrs Peter Leckenby of Culrain for help in choosing the illustrations.

T. and A. D. Poyser have kindly given permission for the reproduction of the sketches (by Donald Watson), figures 2, 8 and 12, and the sonagram (by Bill Sinclair), figure 16. The map, figure 18, is reproduced by permission of the British Trust for Ornithology and T. and A. D. Poyser.

The photographs are acknowledged to: Harold Auger, 13; D. A. P. Cooke, 1; Dennis Green, 5, 9, 11; Eric and David Hosking, the front cover and 3, 4, 6, 10, 14, 15, 17; David Whitaker, 7.

24